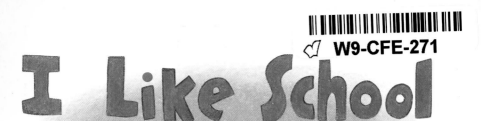

I Like School

Written by Sally Terkel
Illustrated by Annette Cable

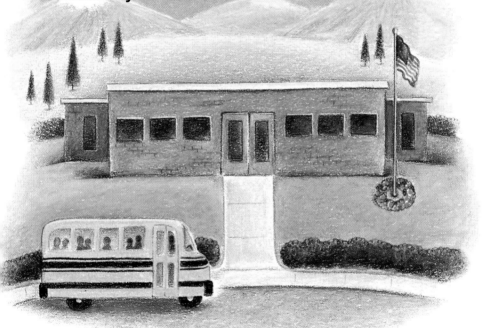

Scott Foresman

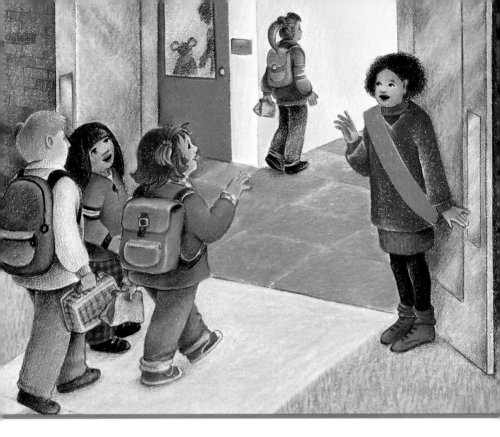

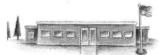

I like to go to school.

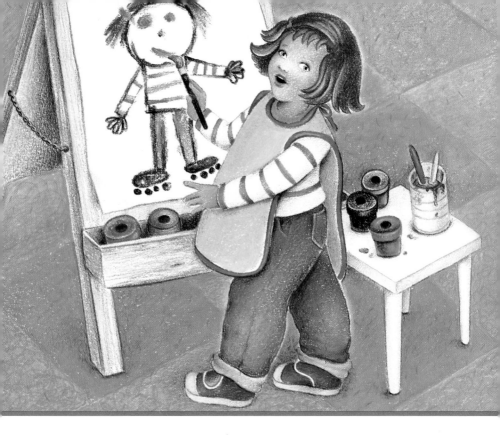

 I like to paint.

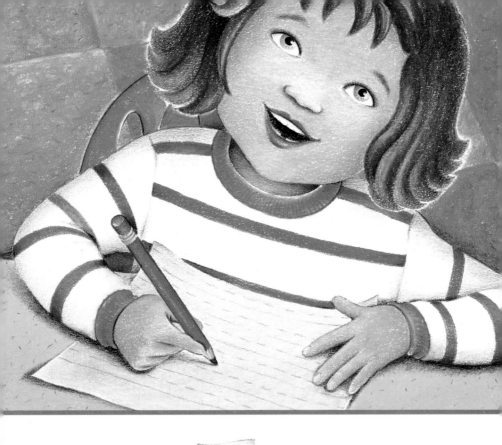

I like to write.

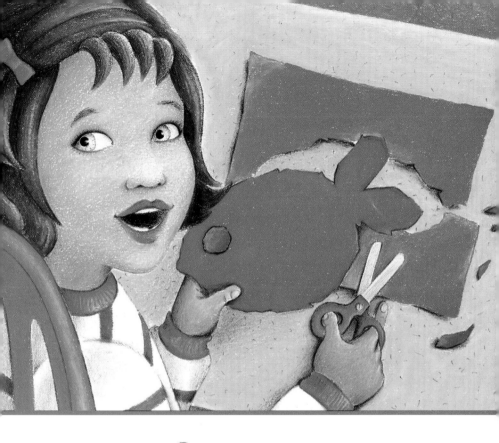

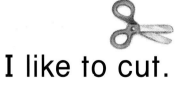
I like to cut.

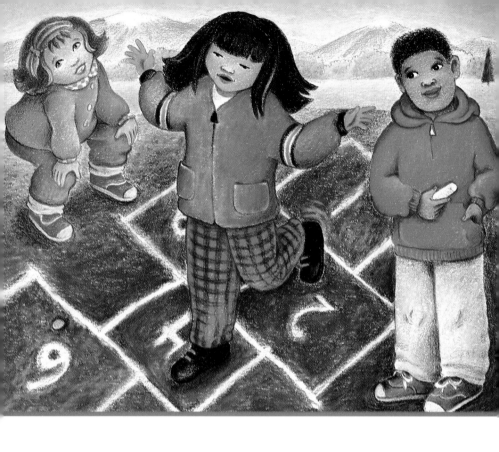

I like to play.

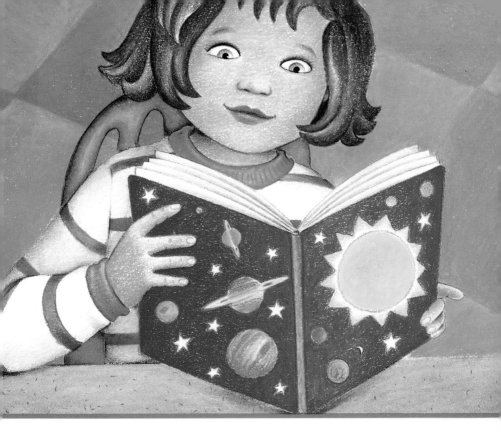

I like to read.

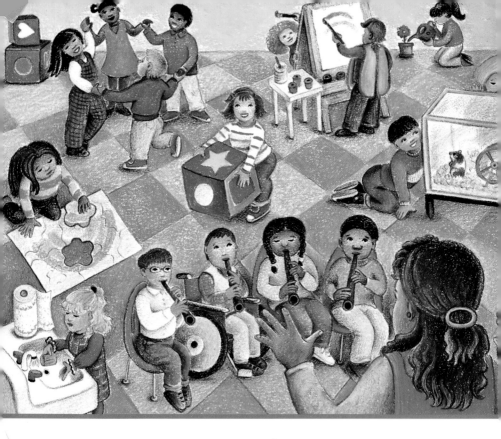

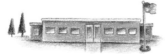

I like school.